rockschool®

Female Vocals
Grade 2

*Performance pieces, technical exercises and in-depth guidance
for Rockschool examinations*

Acknowledgements

Published by Rockschool Ltd. © 2014 under license from Music Sales Ltd.
Catalogue Number RSK091402
ISBN: 978-1-908920-52-2

AUDIO
Backing tracks produced by Music Sales Limited
Supporting test backing tracks recorded by Jon Musgrave, Jon Bishop and Duncan Jordan
Supporting test vocals recorded by Duncan Jordan
Supporting tests mixed at Langlei Studios by Duncan Jordan
Mastered by Duncan Jordan

MUSICIANS
Neal Andrews, Lucie Burns (Lazy Hammock), Jodie Davies,Tenisha Edwards, Noam Lederman,
Beth Loates-Taylor, Dave Marks, Salena Mastroianni, Paul Miro, Ryan Moore, Jon Musgrave,
Chris Smart, Ross Stanley, T-Jay, Stacy Taylor, Daniel Walker

PUBLISHING
Compiled and edited by James Uings, Simon Troup, Stephen Lawson, Stuart Slater
Internal design and layout by Simon and Jennie Troup, Digital Music Art
Cover designed by Philip Millard, Philip Millard Design
Fact Files written by Stephen Lawson, Owen Bailey and Michael Leonard
Additional proofing by Chris Bird, Ronan Macdonald, Jonathan Preiss and Becky Baldwin
Cover photography © IBL / Rex Features
Full transcriptions by Music Sales Ltd.

SYLLABUS
Vocal specialists: Martin Hibbert and Eva Brandt
Additional consultation: Emily Nash, Stuart Slater and Sarah Page
Supporting tests composition: Martin Hibbert, James Uings, Jon Musgrave, Jodie Davies,
Ryan Moore, Chris Hawkins, Jonathan Preiss
Rhythmic test lyrics: Lucie Burns (Lazy Hammock)

PRINTING
Printed and bound in the United Kingdom by Caligraving Ltd.
Media hosting by Dropcards

DISTRIBUTION
Exclusive Distributors: Music Sales Ltd.

CONTACTING ROCKSCHOOL
www.rockschool.co.uk
Telephone: +44 (0)845 460 4747
Fax: +44 (0)845 460 1960

Table of Contents

Introductions & Information

Page

Rockschool Grade Pieces

Page

Technical Exercises

Page

Supporting Tests

Page

Additional Information

Page

Welcome to Rockschool Female Vocals Grade 2

Welcome to the Rockschool Female Vocals Grade 2 pack. This book and accompanying download card contain everything you need to sing at this grade.

Vocals Exams

At each grade you have the option of taking one of two different types of examination:

- **Grade Exam:** a Grade Exam is a mixture of music performances, technical work and tests. You prepare three pieces (two of which may be Free Choice Pieces) and the contents of the Technical Exercise section. This accounts for 75% of the exam marks. The other 25% consists of: *either* a Sight Reading *or* an Improvisation & Interpretation test (10%), two Ear Tests (10%), and finally you will be asked five General Musicianship Questions (5%). The pass mark is 60%.

- **Performance Certificate:** in a Performance Certificate you sing five pieces. Up to three of these can be Free Choice Pieces. Each song is marked out of 20 and the pass mark is 60%.

Book Contents

The book is divided into a number of sections. These are:

- **Exam Pieces:** in this book you will find six well-known pieces of Grade 2 standard. Each song is preceded by a Fact File detailing information about the original recording, the artist who sang on it and some recommended listening if you wish to research the artist further.

- **Piano and guitar notation:** every exam piece is printed with a piano part and guitar chords. Both are a representation of the overall band arrangement. These have been included to assist you with your practice should you wish to use a piano and/or guitar for accompaniment. In your exam you must perform to the backing tracks provided.

- **Vocal score:** in addition to the piano/vocal/guitar arrangement there is also a separate vocal-only score to allow you to view the vocal part on a single sheet of paper.

- **Technical Exercises:** there are a range of technical exercises in this grade. Some are notated in full, and some give a range of starting notes.

- **Supporting Tests and General Musicianship Questions:** in Vocals Grade 2 there are three supporting tests – *either* a Sight Reading *or* an Improvisation & Interpretation test and two Ear Tests – and a set of General Musicianship Questions (GMQs) asked at the end of each exam. Examples of the types of tests likely to appear in the exam are printed in this book.

- **General Information:** finally, you will find information on exam procedures, including online examination entry, marking schemes, information on Free Choice Pieces and improvisation requirements for each grade.

Audio

Each song in Vocals Grade 2 has an audio track that can be downloaded via the download card that comes with the book. This is a backing track with the vocal taken off so you can sing along with the band. The backing tracks should be used in examinations. There are also audio examples of the supporting tests printed in the book.

The audio files are supplied in MP3 format, the most widely compatible audio format in common usage – MP3s will likely be familiar to anyone with a computer, iPod, smartphone or similar device. Once downloaded you will be able to play them on any compatible device; we hope that you find this extra versatility useful.

Download cards

Download cards are easy to use – simply go to *www.dropcards.com/rsvocals* and type in the code on the back of your card. It's best to do this somewhere with a good connection, to ensure that the download is uninterrupted. If you have any problems with your download, you should be able to resolve them at *www.dropcards.com/help*.

We hope you enjoy using this book. You can find further details about Rockschool's Vocals and other instrumental syllabuses on our website: *www.rockschool.co.uk*.

SONG TITLE: CALL ME
ALBUM: N/A
RELEASED: 1980
LABEL: CHRYSALIS
GENRE: NEW WAVE

PERSONNEL: DEBBIE HARRY (VOX)
CHRIS STEIN (GTR)
FRANK INFANTE (GTR)
NIGEL HARRISON (BASS)
CLEM BURKE (DRUMS)
JIMMY DESTRI (KEYS)

UK CHART PEAK: 1
US CHART PEAK: 1

BACKGROUND INFO

'Call Me' was a single released by the American new wave band Blondie in 1980. It was the group's fourth Number 1 in the UK and second in America.

THE BIGGER PICTURE

Blondie formed in New York in 1974. The band was part of the 'new wave' of groups that emerged after punk who retained the attitude of punk rock but incorporated other sounds and genres too. Singer Debbie Harry was a former Playboy Bunny whose sex appeal gave the band its name (after passing truckers' shouts of 'Hey blondie!'). Blondie's self-titled debut album was released on the independent label Private Stock Records to little fanfare in 1976. However, in 1977 Chrysalis Records bought out Blondie's contract with Private Stock, reissued their debut album and released its follow-up, *Plastic Letters*. Two singles from their sophomore, 'Denis' and '(I'm Always Touched By Your) Presence, Dear', charted in the UK and the group turned to British producer Mike Chapman to record their third album, the classic, commercially successful *Parallel Lines*, released in 1978. The hits kept on coming until the band split up in 1982. Blondie reformed in the 1990s and continue to tour to this day.

NOTES

'Call Me' was written by the groundbreaking electronic musician and producer Giorgio Moroder, who had a hit with Donna Summer's 'I Feel Love' in 1977 and featured more recently on Daft Punk's *Random Access Memories*. Moroder had been commissioned to compose the theme song for the film *American Gigolo*, starring Richard Gere. He had originally approached Stevie Nicks from Fleetwood Mac to collaborate on a then instrumental track he was calling 'Man Machine', but due to contractual obligations, Nicks was unable to commit. Debbie Harry was then asked to come up with lyrics and a melody – a process she says took just a few hours. The track was then re-recorded from scratch with the rest of Blondie playing their instruments and Moroder in the producer's chair.

RECOMMENDED LISTENING

'The Tide Is High' was Blondie's 1980 cover of a reggae song by The Paragons that went to Number 1 in America and Britain. 'Atomic' is the band at its dark, disco-imbued best, while 'Maria', released during the group's comeback in the 1990s is simply classic guitar pop. *Atomic: The Very Best Of Blondie* is a worthy addition to any record collection.

Call Me

Blondie

Words by Deborah Harry
Music by Giorgio Moroder

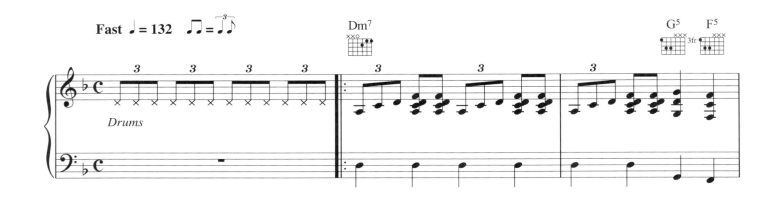

1. Col - our me___ your col - our, ba - by;
2. Cov - er me___ with kiss - es, ba - by;

col - our me___ your car.___
cov - er me___ with love.___

Col - our me___ your col - our, dar - ling;
Roll me in___ de - sign - er sheets,___ I'll

an - y place, an - y - where,___ an - y - way.___ An - y - time,

an - y place,___ an - y - where,___ an - y - day.___

me, my love;___ call me, call me in a sweet de-sign.___ Call

me, call me for your lov-er's lov-er's al - i - bi.___ Call

me on the line,___ call me, call me an - y, an-y-time.___ Call

Repeat and fade

me! Oh, call me, ooh,___ ooh,___ ah.___ Call

SONG TITLE: POKER FACE
ALBUM: THE FAME
RELEASED: 2008
LABEL: INTERSCOPE
GENRE: POP

PERSONNEL: STEFANI GERMANOTTA (VOX)

UK CHART PEAK: 1
US CHART PEAK: 1

BACKGROUND INFO

'Poker Face' was the second single from Lady Gaga's debut album, *The Fame*. It has sold more than 14 million copies worldwide, making it one of the best-selling singles of all time.

THE BIGGER PICTURE

Lady Gaga was born Stefani Germanotta in New York City in 1986. She played piano from a young age and performed in high school theatre productions. After high school, Germanotta studied musical theatre at New York University, where she developed an interest in modern art. In her second year of university, she quit to focus on her music. For the next few years Germanotta performed on the New York music scene with friends from university under the name The Stefani Germanotta (or SG) Band. A video on YouTube shows the SG Band performing a competent but uninspired cover of Led Zeppelin's 'D'Yer Maker' – Germanotta's transformation from talented former performing arts student to 'pop art' queen was yet to happen…

In 2006 she came to the attention of manager/producer Rob Fusari, who took her under his wing. The pair began a musical partnership that produced the songs 'Paparazzi' and 'Beautiful, Dirty, Rich'. Fusari gave Germanotta the nickname 'Radio Gaga' after quipping that her harmonies reminded him of Queen. 'Lady Gaga' was the result of a predictive text error. Germanotta loved it and insisted on being called 'Lady Gaga' from then on.

NOTES

Gaga's first two singles, 'Just Dance' and 'Poker Face', were co-written with RedOne just months after the Swedish producer had been on the verge of flying home to Sweden, his dream of making it in America having foundered. Just as RedOne had been thinking of packing his suitcase, he got a break producing for the singer Kat De Luna and was introduced to Lady Gaga by his (and Gaga's) manager Rob Fusari. It was an inspired pairing, as 'Just Dance' and 'Poker Face' were each written in under an hour and launched the careers of RedOne and Gaga…

RECOMMENDED LISTENING

'Just Dance' is in the same synth pop vein as 'Poker Face'. 'Paparazzi' was co-written with Rob Fusari and is a piano ballad given a synth-pop spin. All three can be found on Gaga's excellent debut, *The Fame* (2008).

Poker Face

Lady Gaga

Words & Music by Stefani Germanotta & Nadir Khayat

G♯m
E/G♯
F♯
fold 'em, let 'em hit me, raise it. Ba - by, stay with me.
A lit - tle gam - bl - in' is fun when you're with me.
G♯m
E/G♯
F♯
Luck and in - tu - i - tion play the cards with spades to start. And
Rus - sian Rou - lette is not the same with - out a gun. And,
G♯m
E/G♯
F♯
af - ter he's been hooked, I'll play the one that's on his heart.
ba - by, when it's love, if it's not rough it is - n't fun.
G♯m
E/G♯
F♯
G♯m
Oh, whoa, oh, oh, oh, oh, oh. I'll get him hot, show
4fr

SONG TITLE: PRICE TAG
ALBUM: WHO YOU ARE
RELEASED: 2011
LABEL: ISLAND
GENRE: POP

PERSONNEL: JESSIE J (VOX)
B.O.B. (VOX)
DR. LUKE (DRUMS+KEYS)
BUTCH COLEMAN (BASS)

UK CHART PEAK: 1
US CHART PEAK: 23

BACKGROUND INFO

'Price Tag' was the second single from Jessie J's debut album, *Who You Are*. Its upbeat production and 'money isn't everything' theme sent it to Number 1 but also ruffled a few feathers…

THE BIGGER PICTURE

Jessica Ellen Cornish was born in London in 1988. Her sisters, both older, were academic and she was expected to follow in their footsteps, but from a young age Cornish was drawn to more creative activities. "Give me something to draw or an outfit to pick for someone, or hair, make-up, acting, write a song, I'm fine with it," she said, "but anything to do with sums – it was never my thing." A natural performer, at the age of 11 she was cast in a production of Andrew Lloyd Webber's *Whistle Down The Wind* in London's West End. From there she went on to study musical theatre at the famous BRIT School, alma mater of Adele, Leona Lewis and Amy Winehouse. Next she joined a girl group called Soul Deep and began writing songs professionally, which led to a publishing deal with Sony ATV while she was still in her teens. In the following years, she wrote for artists such as Miley Cyrus and Taio Cruz, and had her music featured in a Nivea commercial.

NOTES

Jessica Cornish began work on her debut album, *Who You Are*, in 2005 and spent the next six years crafting a record worthy of any major artist (renaming herself 'Jessie J' along the way). 'Price Tag' was produced by Dr. Luke and co-written with Claude Kelly, who J had worked with previously on the Miley Cyrus song 'Party In The U.S.A.' 'Price Tag''s lyrics were criticised by some, who accused Jessie J of hypocrisy, their perception being 'Here's a rich, successful pop star telling the rest of us money doesn't matter'. J responded in an interview: "['Price Tag' is] not me saying that you can live for free, because obviously that isn't the case; but I'm saying that you don't always have to let it be about that [money and possessions]. It isn't always about how much your shoes cost. It's about the fact that you even have a pair of shoes to walk in."

RECOMMENDED LISTENING

Jessie J's first single, 'Do It Like A Dude', was written for (but never used by) Rihanna and inspired by the latter's 'Dirty Boy'. 'Domino' was another hit with its funky guitar riff and vocal gymnastics. 'It's My Party' followed in the same mould, another major key belter oozing personality.

Price Tag

Jessie J

Words & Music by Lukasz Gottwald, Claude Kelly,
Bobby Ray Simmons & Jessica Cornish

Female Vocals Grade 2

Amy Winehouse

SONG TITLE: REHAB
ALBUM: BACK TO BLACK
RELEASED: 2006
LABEL: ISLAND
GENRE: R&B

PERSONNEL: AMY WINEHOUSE (VOX)

UK CHART PEAK: 7
US CHART PEAK: 9

BACKGROUND INFO

'Rehab' was the first single from Amy Winehouse's second studio album, *Back To Black*. It was her first Top 40 single in Britain.

THE BIGGER PICTURE

Amy Winehouse was born in London in 1983. She grew up listening to jazz, to which she was introduced by members of her family, including her dad Mitch and her grandmother, a singer who once dated famous English jazz musician Ronnie Scott. It was her grandmother who saw Winehouse's potential and suggested she attend a theatre school on Saturdays. While attending said school, Winehouse developed an interest in hip hop and R'n'B, and started a short-lived rap group with her friend. These early influences – jazz and urban – were to stay with Winehouse throughout her life, making their mark on her debut album, *Frank* (2003), with its jazz leanings and hip hop producer in Salaam Remi, and on her last studio album, *Back To Black* (2006). The latter was Winehouse's commercial breakthrough, a record that turned to classic soul and R&B for its influences. In doing so it went to the top of album charts around the world and made Winehouse an international star before her death, at the age of 27, in 2011.

NOTES

'Rehab' was, like many of Amy Winehouse's songs, written about the singer's own experiences – in this case of being told by her management company to attend an alcohol rehabilitation centre. "When it was suggested to me," said Winehouse, "I went to see the guy at the centre for 10 minutes just so I could say to the record company that I went. I literally walked in and walked out. I knew it wasn't for me." Shortly after, Winehouse split from her management. During her stay in New York while working on her album *Back To Black*, Winehouse recounted the story to the album's producer Mark Ronson. While sympathetic to the singer's situation, Ronson couldn't help but be inspired by Winehouse's spoken "No, no, no", which became the song's hook at the producer's behest.

RECOMMENDED LISTENING

Amy Winehouse's first album, *Frank*, is an interesting place to go to hear the singer's jazz and hip hop influences. However, her finest moment was its follow-up, *Back To Black*. It won Best Pop Vocal Album at the Grammy Awards in 2008, produced five hit singles and has sold over 3.5 million copies in the UK alone. Standout tracks include 'Rehab', 'Back To Black' and 'Love Is A Losing Game'.

Rehab

Amy Winehouse
Words & Music by Amy Winehouse

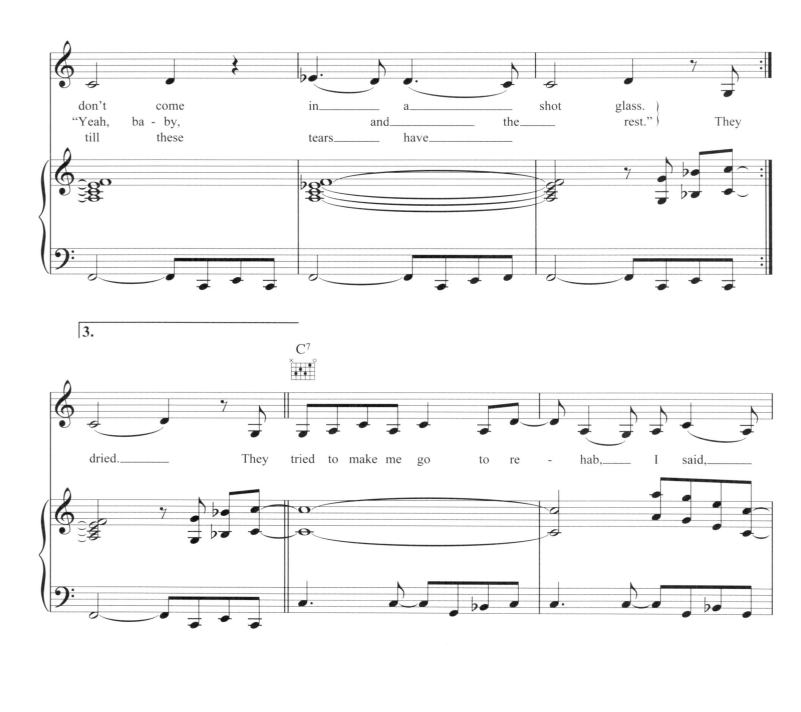

don't come in_____ a_____ shot glass.
"Yeah, ba - by, and_____ the_____ rest." They
till these tears_____ have_____

dried._____ They tried to make me go to re - hab,_____ I said,_____

no,_____ no,_____ no. Yes_____ I've been black but when_

Cyndi Lauper

SONG TITLE: TRUE COLORS

ALBUM: TRUE COLORS

RELEASED: 1986

LABEL: EPIC

GENRE: POP

PERSONNEL: CYNDI LAUPER (VOX)

UK CHART PEAK: 12

US CHART PEAK: 1

BACKGROUND INFO

'True Colors' was the title track and first single released from Cyndi Lauper's second album.

THE BIGGER PICTURE

Cynthia 'Cindy' Lauper was born in New York in 1953. As a teenager she wrote her own songs and dropped out of high school aged 17 to perform in covers bands. Eventually Lauper strained her voice and had to attend vocal lessons to repair it. In 1977 she formed the band Blue Angel with John Turi. They released an album in 1980, which flopped, and the group disbanded. Lauper continued to sing in clubs and restaurants in the New York area, where she was spotted by manager (and later, Lauper's boyfriend) David Wolff. Wolff got Lauper signed to Portrait Records, who released her debut album, *She's So Unusual*, in 1983.

NOTES

'True Colors' was the only original song on Lauper's second album that she didn't have a hand in writing. Instead, it was written by the songwriters Tom Kelly and Billy Steinberg whose other hits include 'So Emotional' (for Whitney Houston), 'Alone' (originally for their own band i-Ten, then famously for Heart) and 'Eternal Flame' (The Bangles). Steinberg wrote the song originally about his mother: "Cyndi Lauper came up with a very creative departure from our demo. The demo was rooted in the gospel ballad tradition of a song like 'Bridge Over Troubled Water', 'Let It Be' or 'Lean On Me', that sort of thing with the piano. Cyndi completely dismantled that arrangement and came up with something that was breathtaking and stark." As well as proving a hit for Lauper, it has been covered since by Phil Collins and Eva Cassidy. It was Lauper's last Number 1 single.

RECOMMENDED LISTENING

'Girls Just Wanna Have Fun' was Cyndi Lauper's first hit and the lead single off her debut solo album, *She's So Unusual*. 'Girls...' has been described as a 'feminist anthem' even though it was originally written by a man from a male perspective – before being given a feminine twist by Lauper. Musically, it's evocative of its time, with a popular spin on the new wave sound. 'Time After Time' was from the same album as 'True Colors' and is another classic ballad that was a hit for Lauper. To hear another side of Cyndi Lauper vocally, try her later album *Memphis Blues* (2010).

True Colors

Cyndi Lauper

Words & Music by Billy Steinberg & Tom Kelly

SONG TITLE: YOUR SONG
ALBUM: BRIGHT LIGHTS
RELEASED: 2010
LABEL: POLYDOR
GENRE: POP

PERSONNEL: ELLIE GOULDING (VOX)
BEN LOVETT (VARIOUS)
RUTH DE TURBERVILLE (CELLO)
MATT WIGGINS (TIMPANI)

UK CHART PEAK: 2
US CHART PEAK: N/A

BACKGROUND INFO

'Your Song' is Ellie Goulding's cover of an Elton John song written by John and Bernie Taupin.

THE BIGGER PICTURE

Elena Jane Goulding was born in 1986 in a small village in Herefordshire. She began playing the clarinet at the age of nine, then took guitar lessons when she turned 14. Within a year of picking up the guitar she was writing her own folk-inspired songs and later won a singing contest at her local college – a promising start. While studying drama at the University of Kent, Goulding discovered electronic music and began to develop her unique sound. Before she could finish her studies, Goulding was discovered by the artist management company Turn First Artists, who insisted she leave university, move to London and focus on her music. She was introduced to the producer Starsmith and the pair began working on the material that would form her debut album, *Lights*. It was a winning combination, as *Lights* debuted at Number 1 on the UK album charts in 2010. Since then, Goulding has released an expanded edition of her debut entitled *More Lights*, featuring the song of the same name, and her second album, *Halcyon*, (another UK chart topper) in 2012.

NOTES

'Your Song' was one of Elton John and Bernie Taupin's early collaborations. It is said to have been dashed out over breakfast one morning, and at first glance you could believe it. Its lyrics are simple – even naive – and at times clumsy, but what makes them great is these apparent foibles are actually devices to show the innocence of the song's protagonist. Hence faltering lines like 'If I was a sculptor, but then again, no'. No less a songwriter than John Lennon praised 'Your Song' in a 1975 interview with *Rolling Stone*: "I remember hearing it in America and thinking, 'Great, that's the first new thing that's happened since we (The Beatles) happened.' It was a step forward."

RECOMMENDED LISTENING

Ellie Goulding's version of 'Your Song' has a charm about it that's entirely down to her tender vocal performance. 'Anything Could Happen' is more typical Goulding: heavily effected vocals matched with an uplifting lyric and chord progression. 'Burn' was Goulding's first single to reach Number 1 in the Top 40 with its synth-heavy production and choppy phrasing. 'How Long Will I Love', by contrast, is a piano ballad with vulnerable-sounding vocals, which should appeal if you like her version of 'Your Song'.

Your Song

Ellie Goulding
Words & Music by Elton John & Bernie Taupin

8vb throughout

1. It's a lit-tle bit fun-ny, this feel-ing in-side.__
2. So ex-cuse me for-get-ting, but these things I do.__

I'm not one of those__ who__ can eas-i-ly hide.__
See, I've for-got-ten__ if they're green or they're blue.__

I don't have much mon-ey but boy, if I did
An-y-way the thing is, what I real-ly mean,

Technical Exercises

Group A: Scales

The natural minor scale must be prepared as shown below. You may select any starting note from A–E. You will be asked if you would like to sing along to a metronome click or hear four clicks before you start. Whichever option you choose, you will hear your chosen starting note before the count starts. You may perform this test using any vocal sound except humming or whistling. The tempo is ♩=80.

Group B: Arpeggios

In this group, both of the arpeggio exercises need to be prepared as shown below. You will be asked to perform one of them in the exam, as chosen by the examiner.

This test is performed to a metronome click track and you may select any starting note from A–E. You will hear the root note played on piano followed by a one-bar (three or four clicks) count-in. You may perform this test using any vocal sound except humming or whistling. The tempo is ♩=80.

A minor arpeggio | Pattern 1

A minor arpeggio | Pattern 2

Group C: Intervals

In this group, both the major 3rd and minor 3rd intervals need to be prepared as below. You will be asked to perform one of them in the exam, as chosen by the examiner.

The examiner will choose a starting note within the range A–C. You will hear this note followed by a four-beat count-in. You may perform this test using any vocal sound except humming or whistling. The tempo is ♩=90.

Major 3rd interval

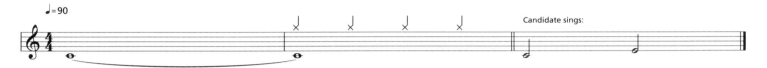

Minor 3rd interval

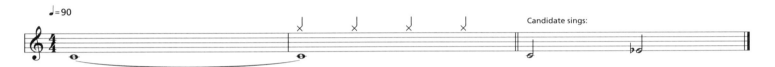

Group D: Technical Studies

This group consists of two Technical Studies: one rhythmic and one melodic. The examiner will ask you to perform one in the exam. The examiner will decide which, so you must prepare *both* before the exam. The rhythmic test starts with a four-beat count. The melodic test starts with the root note followed by a four-beat count. Both tests should be performed to the appropriate backing track which can be found on the download card.

1. Rhythmic | Rhythmic accuracy

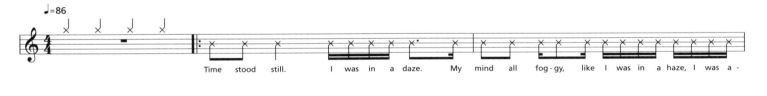

2. Melodic | Dynamic change

Sight Reading

In this section you have a choice between:

- *Either* – a sight reading test
- *Or* – an improvisation and interpretation test (see facing page).

The examiner will ask you which one you wish to choose before commencing. Once you have decided, you cannot change your mind.

The examiner will give you a four-bar melody in the key of F major or A minor covering a range up to a major 3rd. You will be given 90 seconds to practise, after which you will perform the test. The tempo is ♩=70.

During the practice time you will be given the choice of a metronome click throughout or a count-in of four beats at the beginning. Whichever option you choose, the practice time will start with the examiner playing the root note. You will receive the same choice when performing the test. The test will start with the root note.

You may perform this test using any vocal sound except humming or whistling.

Please note: the test shown is an example. The examiner will give you a different version in the exam.

Improvisation & Interpretation

The examiner will give you a chord sequence in the key of A minor. You must improvise a melody over the backing track. You will hear the backing track three times. The first and second time is for you to rehearse and the third time is for you to perform the final version for the exam. Each playthrough will begin with the root note and a four-beat count-in. The backing track is continuous throughout, so once the first playthrough has finished, the root note and count-in of the second and third playthroughs will start immediately. The tempo is ♩=80–90.

You may perform this test using any vocal sound except humming or whistling.

Please note: the test shown is an example. The examiner will give you a different version in the exam.

Ear Tests

In this section, there are two ear tests:
- Melodic Recall
- Rhythmic Recall

You will find one example of each type of test printed below and you will be given both of them in the exam.

Test 1 | Melodic Recall
The examiner will play you a two-bar melody played to a drum backing. It will use the first three notes of the C major scale and the first note will be the root note. You will hear the test twice. Each time the test is played, it is preceded by the root note and a four-beat count-in. There will be a short gap for you to practise after each playthrough. Next you will hear a *vocal* count-in, after which you should sing the melody to the drum backing. The tempo is ♩=85.

It is acceptable to sing over the track as it is being played as well as practising after the first two playthroughs. The length of time available after the second playthrough is pre-recorded on the audio track, so the count-in may begin while you are still practising.

You may perform this test using any vocal sound except humming or whistling.

Please note: the test shown is an example. The examiner will give you a different version in the exam.

Test 2 | Rhythmic Recall
This test comes in two parts:

Part 1 | Rhythmic Recall
The examiner will play you a two-bar rhythm played on a single note to a drum backing. You will hear the test twice. Each time the test is played, it is preceded by a four-beat count-in. There will be a short gap for you to practise after each playthrough. Next you will hear a *vocal* count-in, after which you should sing the rhythm back. The tempo is ♩=90.

For this exercise, use 'da' or 'ba' vocal sounds.

It is acceptable to sing over the track as it is being played as well as practising after the first two playthroughs. The length of time available after the second playthrough is pre-recorded on the audio track, so the count-in may begin while you are still practising.

Part 2 | Identification
You will then be asked to identify the rhythm heard in part 1 from two printed examples shown to you by the examiner.

Please note: the test shown is an example. The examiner will give you a different version in the exam.

General Musicianship Questions

In this part of the exam you will be asked five questions. Four of these will be about general music knowledge and the fifth will be about your voice.

Part 1 | General Music Knowledge

The examiner will ask four music knowledge questions from the categories below. The questions will be based on one of the pieces (including Free Choice Pieces) as performed by you in the exam. You can choose which one.

If there are handwritten notes on the piece you have chosen, the examiner may ask you to choose an alternative.

You will be *asked to identify:*
- Any pitch name. (You will not need to state flat, sharp or natural).
- Whole-, half-, quarter-, eighth- and 16th-note values.
- Any rest value.

You will be asked to *identify and explain:*
- The meaning of the 4/4 time signature marking.
- The meaning of repeat marks, first and second time bars.
- The meaning of staccato marks.
- The meaning of slurs.

Part 2 | Your Voice

The examiner will also ask you one question about your voice. Brief demonstrations to assist your answer are acceptable.

You will be asked:
- What is the meaning of 'diction'?
- What is the meaning of 'tone'?
- During a song, when would be a better time to take a breath?
- Why is posture important when singing?

Entering Exams, Exam Procedure & Marking Schemes

Entering Exams

Entering a Rockschool exam is easy. You can enter online at *www.rockschool.co.uk* or by downloading and filling in an exam entry form. The full Rockschool examination terms and conditions as well as exam periods and current fees are available from our website or by calling +44 (0)845 460 4747.

Exam procedure

In the exam you can decide whether to start with the Performance Pieces or the Technical Exercises. These will be followed by the Supporting Tests (Ear Tests and Quick Study Pieces) and General Musicianship Questions.

Use Of Microphone

At Level 1 (Grades 1–3) microphone use is optional, although candidates may use one if they feel it will enhance their performance. At Level 2 (Grades 4–5) microphone use is obligatory for all pieces and at Level 3 (Grades 6–8) for the whole exam.

Marking Schemes

Below are the marking schemes for the two different types of Rockschool exam.

GRADE EXAMS | GRADES 1–5

ELEMENT	PASS	MERIT	DISTINCTION
Performance Piece 1	12–14 out of 20	15–17 out of 20	18+ out of 20
Performance Piece 2	12–14 out of 20	15–17 out of 20	18+ out of 20
Performance Piece 3	12–14 out of 20	15–17 out of 20	18+ out of 20
Technical Exercises	9–10 out of 15	11–12 out of 15	13+ out of 15
Either Sight Reading *or* Improvisation & Interpretation	6 out of 10	7–8 out of 10	9+ out of 10
Ear Tests	6 out of 10	7–8 out of 10	9+ out of 10
General Musicianship Questions	3 out of 5	4 out of 5	5 out of 5
TOTAL MARKS	60%+	74%+	90%+

PERFORMANCE CERTIFICATES | GRADES 1–8

ELEMENT	PASS	MERIT	DISTINCTION
Performance Piece 1	12–14 out of 20	15–17 out of 20	18+ out of 20
Performance Piece 2	12–14 out of 20	15–17 out of 20	18+ out of 20
Performance Piece 3	12–14 out of 20	15–17 out of 20	18+ out of 20
Performance Piece 4	12–14 out of 20	15–17 out of 20	18+ out of 20
Performance Piece 5	12–14 out of 20	15–17 out of 20	18+ out of 20
TOTAL MARKS	60%+	75%+	90%+

Improvisation Requirements & Free Choice Pieces

At Rockschool it is our aim to encourage creativity and individualism. We therefore give candidates the opportunity to express themselves musically within styles of their own choice. For this reason, Free Choice Pieces are accepted in all Vocals grades. In addition, all songs performed in exams from Grade 3 onwards have compulsory improvisation requirements.

Improvisation Requirements

From Grade 3, all songs, whether from the grade book or chosen as FCPs, need to incorporate improvisation. The improvisation can be prepared in advance, but is expected to be individually constructed, and needs to include **both** vocal ad-libbing and re-working of existing melody lines as follows:

Level 1 Grade 3: Vocal ad-libbing (2–4 bars) and re-working of melody line (4 bars)
Level 2 Grades 4–5: Vocal ad-libbing (4–8 bars) and re-working of melody line (4–8 bars)
Level 3 Grades 6–7: Vocal ad-libbing (8–12 bars) and re-working of melody line (8 bars)
Level 3 Grades 8: Vocal ad-libbing (12–16 bars) and re-working of melody line (8 bars)

For all pieces, you will need to highlight the sheet music to show the examiner the location of both ad-libbed and re-worked parts at the beginning of the exam.

Notes

- You are free to choose where you improvise. However, in all cases, improvisations need to be a continuous number of bars, not a number of smaller bars which in total add up to the ranges shown.

- Vocal ad-lib could be demonstrated in, for example, introductions, endings or open instrumental parts.

- Re-working of a melody could be demonstrated by altering any existing singing parts; for example, verses, choruses, bridges.

- For both ad-lib and re-working of a melody, you need to demonstrate an awareness of harmony, melody, phrasing, use of rhythms and incorporation of any appropriate expression in a stylistically appropriate manner. Range and content will be expected to increase progressively as you move through the grades.

- We would encourage re-working to take place later in a piece after the original has been presented to show you can portray the original, then you are able to adapt appropriately with individual colour.

- Improvisation can be a good place to demonstrate your head voice, which can often be omitted, reducing the technical content of a piece at a particular grade.

Free Choice Pieces (FCPs)

An FCP is defined as any piece outside the grade book, and can fall into two categories:

1) **Wider Repertoire:** a full list of pre-approved and regularly updated pieces can be found on *www.rockschool.co.uk*. These songs can be used *without* prior approval from Rockschool.

2) **Own Choice:** candidates can choose any song in any genre outside the grade book and wider repertoire. These songs can, however, only be used *with* prior approval from Rockschool. This requirement is compulsory and you need to contact the office to have your chosen piece(s) approved. Please allow five weeks before your exam to receive a decision.

We cannot accept any songs which have not been approved or are not contained in the grade book or wider repertoire.

For all grades, candidates can choose the following number of FCPs in the exam:
Grade Examinations: Up to 2 of 3 pieces can be free choice. (At least one piece must be from the grade book.)
Performance Certificates: Up to 3 of 5 pieces can be free choice. (At least two pieces must be from the grade book.)

For all FCPs, candidates will need to bring the sheet music and a backing track (without vocal part) on the day. A memory stick, iPod or CD/DVD is acceptable and we would also suggest a second source to be safe. It will not be necessary to bring the sheet music or backing tracks for pieces chosen from the grade book.

Copyright Information

Call Me
(Harry/Moroder)
Sony/ATV Harmony UK/Chrysalis Music Limited

Poker Face
(Germanotta/Khayat)
Sony/ATV Music Publishing (UK) Limited

Price Tag
(Gottwald/Kelly/Simmons/Cornish)
Kobalt Music Publishing Limited/Warner/Chappell Music North America Limited/Universal/MCA Music Limited
/Sony/ATV Music Publishing (UK) Limited

Rehab
(Winehouse)
EMI Music Publishing Limited

True Colors
(Steinberg/Kelly)
Sony/ATV Music Publishing (UK) Limited

Your Song
(John/Taupin)
Universal/Dick James Music Limited

mcps